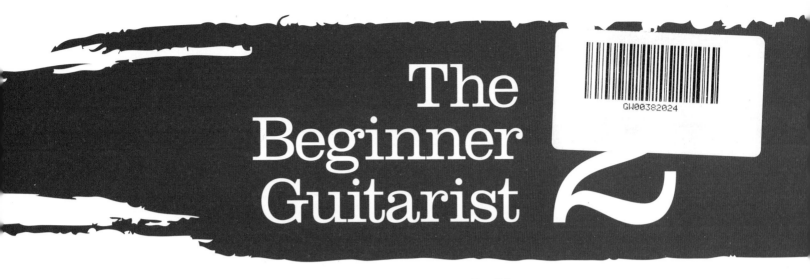

The Beginner Guitarist 2

by Nigel Tuffs

Welcome to The Beginner Guitarist Book Two!

This book aims to build on solid right and left-hand techniques and covers further progress in notation recognition.

It begins with the introduction of quavers (eighth notes) and further focus on the free stroke (tirando). This is balanced with the need to keep the rest stroke (apoyando) solid by giving the pupil a chance to play both melody and accompanying parts. Extensive exercises for finger 4, via chords and melody, are included but the main aim is to complete the learning of the notes in first position, taking in several scales and modes along the way. Simple open chords are also given further attention and the book concludes with coverage of chromaticism relating to the bottom three strings.

A daily practice session for the completion of book two, extra repertoire and other helpful information are all available at **www.thebeginnerguitarist.com**.

About the author

Nigel Tuffs is an instrumental teacher with more than 20 years experience in all areas of guitar teaching. Originally a member of several rock bands he completed an honours degree at the Colchester Institute, specialising in composition and performance, and has since worked extensively as a chamber musician, in guitar ensembles, as an accompanist and also as an educator.

Published by
Chester Music Limited
14-15 Berners Street, London W1T 3LJ, UK.

Exclusive Distributors:

Music Sales Limited
Distribution Centre, Newmarket Road,
Bury St Edmunds, Suffolk IP33 3YB, UK.

Music Sales Pty Limited
20 Resolution Drive, Caringbah, NSW 2229, Australia.

Order No. CH79343

ISBN: 978-1-78038-488-7

This book © Copyright 2012 by Chester Music Limited.

Written by Nigel Tuffs

Edited by Adrian Hopkins

Music processed by Paul Ewers Music Design

Design by Fresh Lemon

Printed in the EU

Chester Music

part of The Music Sales Group

London / New York / Paris / Sydney / Copenhagen / Berlin / Madrid / Hong Kong / Tokyo

Rhythm

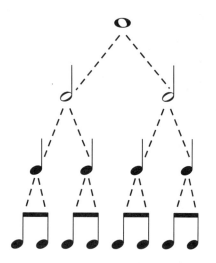

= Semibreve (whole note) = 4 beats

= Minim (half note) = 2 beats

= Crotchet (quarter note) =1 beat

= Quaver (eighth note) = ½ beat

Quavers (eighth notes)
Exercise 1

Exercise 2

Exercise 3

G Major

Freya's Quavers

rest stroke

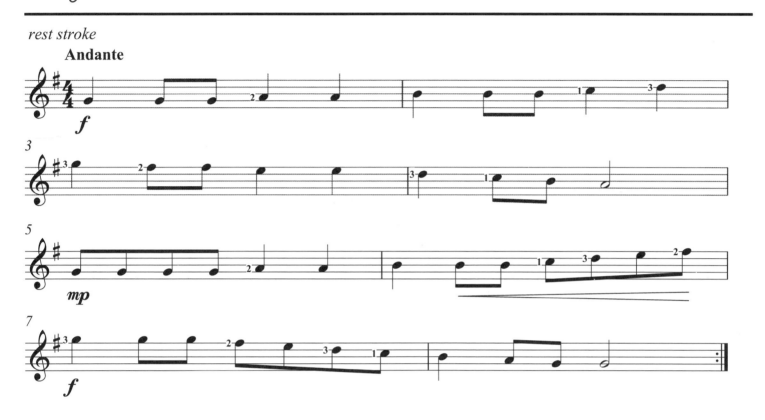

Freya's Quavers Again!

free stroke

TIP: Try playing both pieces on this page as a duet

More Chords

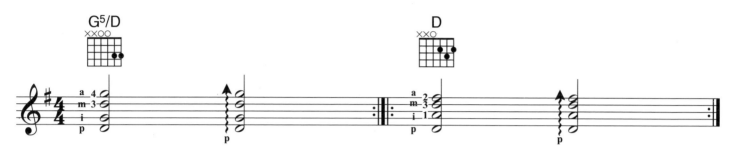

There is more information on chords on page 12

Promenade Rhythm Exercise

Promenade

Exercise for Finger 4

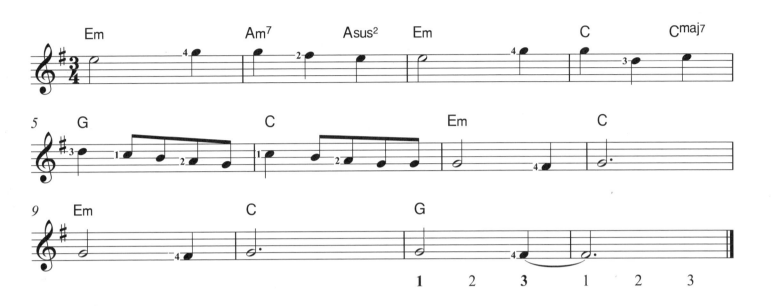

Minuet in G

Johann Sebastian Bach (1685 – 1750)

PIMA

Exercise 1

Exercise 2

Exercise 3

Exercise 4

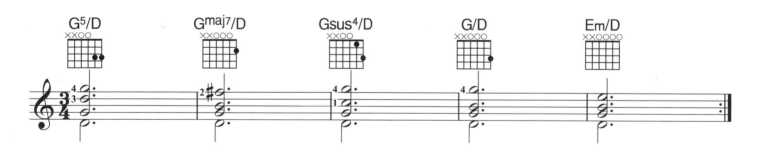

Bright 'n' Sunny Rhythm Exercises

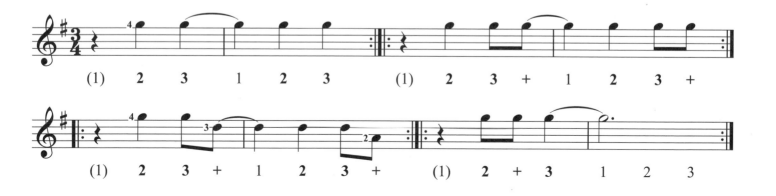

Bright 'n' Sunny Morning

D Natural Minor

It's All Relatively Minor

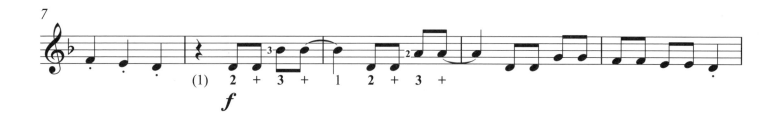

F Major

F G A B♭ C D E F E D C B♭ A G F

It's All Relatively Major

TIP: Try playing both of these pieces as a duet

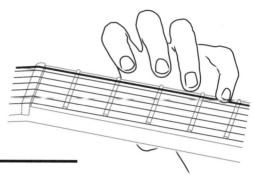

Aeolian Mode (A Natural Minor)

A B C D E F G A G F E D C B A

Zach Attack

Aeolian Mode (A Natural Minor)

Zach Under Attack

TIP: Try playing both of these pieces as a duet

Chord Boxes

o = Open string
x = Do not play

Chord Exercise in E minor

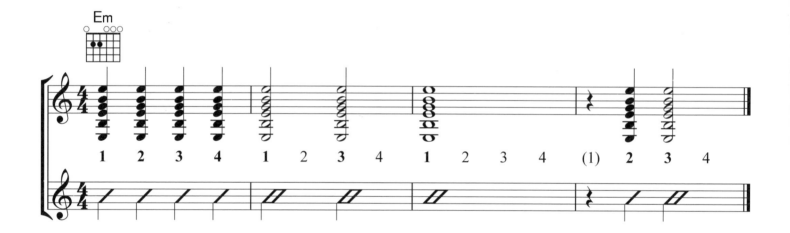

Chord Exercise in A minor

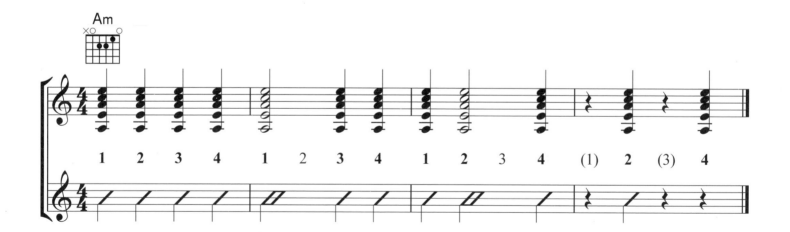

Directions

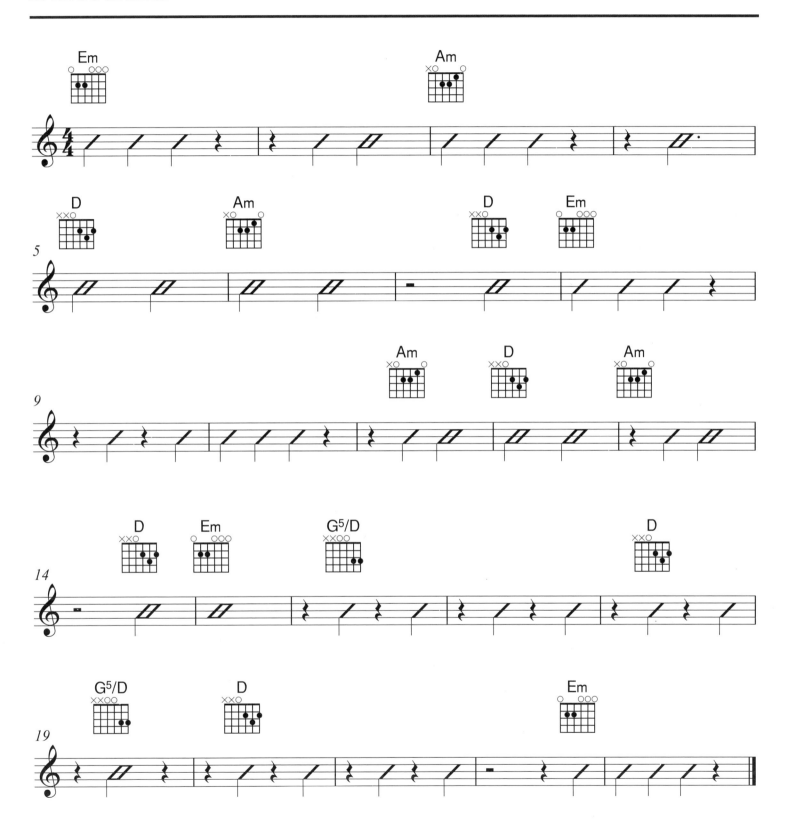

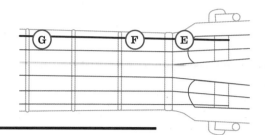

Phrygian Mode

E F G A B C D E F G A B C D E D C B A G F E D C B A G F E

Spanish Dawn

TIP: Look out for the chord in the last bar

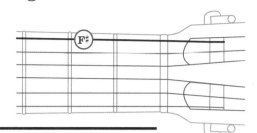

Exercise

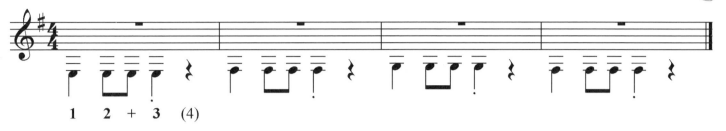

1   2   +   3   (4)

E Natural Minor

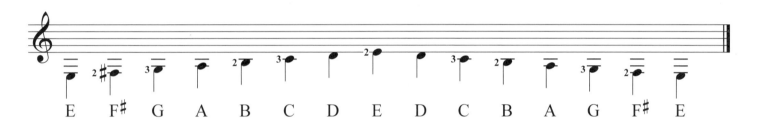

E   F#   G   A   B   C   D   E   D   C   B   A   G   F#   E

Dark Stuff

Chromatic Scale, One Octave E to E

Creepy Chromatic

1 2 3 4 5 6 7 8 9